Princess Collection

AURORA

BELLE

JASMINE

SNOW WHITE

ARIEL

CINDERELLA

Bendon Publishing, International
Ashland, Ohio

Princess Collection

Table of Contents

FLASH CARD INSTRUCTIONS

The flash cards at the end of each story will help your child learn to recognize and practice frequently used words. First, carefully cut out the flash cards. Then, choose three to five cards at a time. Say the word on each card. Then, ask your child to repeat each word. Once your child masters these words, move through the pile in the same manner, continuing to review the words learned earlier.

There are a few other ways for you and your child to use these flash cards for extra practice. Here are a few suggestions:

- Pick the Word—Lay out 5-10 flash cards on a table. Then, say one of the words on the cards. Ask your child to point to the word you've said.
- Make a Sentence—Invite your child to make a sentence from the sight word cards. Have your child look at the illustrations in the story for ideas. Then, have your child choose another card and substitute it for one of the cards in the sentence. Ask your child how the new word changes the meaning of the sentence.
- My Own Sight Words—Have your child make his or her own sight word cards using the writing lines on the back of the cards. Help your child write words that he or she might use regularly, such as family names, your street, your town, or your state. Once your child is able to identify and recognize these words, add them to the "Make a Sentence" game above.

The flash cards in this collection can also be a useful tool as your child completes the activities at the end of each story. If a particular activity seems difficult for your child, use the flash cards to practice the activity first before your child writes.

Walt Disney's
Sleeping Beauty

Adapted by Linda Armstrong

Table of Contents

Long ago in a kingdom far away, a happy king and queen gave a party. It was to celebrate the birth of their daughter Aurora. Three good fairies came to bless the child. Flora gave Aurora the gift of beauty. Fauna gave her the gift of song.

Then the evil Maleficent appeared. She was very angry. "**Oh**, what a shame! You are not happy to see me," **she said**. "There was **no** invitation. I thought that was a mistake. Well, never mind, I have a gift for the child. Yes, she will grow in beauty and grace, but on her sixteenth birthday she will prick her finger on a spinning wheel and die."

The Queen ran to the crib. She hugged her baby.

"Oh, no!" she said.

9

After Maleficent left, the third good fairy gave Aurora her gift. Merryweather **told** King Stefan and the queen she could not **take away** Maleficent's curse. She could only change it. **Aurora** would prick her finger, but **she** would not die. Instead, she would fall into a deep sleep. True Love's Kiss would wake her.

The king did not want **to** take any chances. He ordered his men to burn every spinning wheel in the kingdom. Even after the spinning wheels were gone, the king wanted to do more.

The good fairies said Aurora could live with **them** in the woods until she was sixteen. Maleficent would not be able find her there. The queen wanted Aurora to be safe.

She told them to take Aurora away.

The three fairies lived in the woods as ordinary old women. Aurora lived with them. The king and queen missed their child, but they knew she was safe. After her sixteenth birthday she **would come** home.

At last the great day came.

"Go out and pick us some berries, Aurora," **said** the good fairies.

They wanted time to get ready for her surprise party. As Aurora walked through the woods she sang. A handsome young man was riding through the forest. He heard her. **He** stopped to listen. Then he came over to talk.

They liked each other very much. Aurora asked him to come to the house that night.

He said he would come.

When Aurora came back to the cottage, the fairies gave her a cake and a new dress. Then they told her the best part of her birthday surprise. It was time for her to **go** and live in the castle. They expected Aurora to be happy, but she was not. **She** told them about the young man she met in the woods. She said he was coming **back** to see her.

The good fairies shook their heads sadly. They told her she should not fall in love with him. She was a princess and she **had to** marry a prince. Her real home was the castle.

She had to go back.

When they got to the castle, Maleficent was waiting. It did not take long for the princess to fall under her spell. Following a strange green light, Aurora climbed up the dark tower steps. In the tower room was a spinning wheel. Aurora **had** never seen one before. She reached out to touch it. She could not stop herself.

The room filled with smoke and Maleficent appeared. She had won.

The good fairies hurried through the castle trying **to find** the girl, but they were too late. When they got there, Aurora had fallen into a deep sleep. Only True Love's Kiss could awaken her. The fairies remembered the young man Aurora had met in the woods. **They** were sure Aurora loved **him**.

They had to find him.

The good fairies **got** busy and cast a spell. Everyone would sleep until they found Aurora's true love.

Just before **he** fell asleep, the prince's father said something strange. He said his son was in love **with** a girl from the woods. The good fairies remembered what Aurora said about the young man in the woods. Then they understood. Prince Phillip was Aurora's true love!

Flora, Fauna, and Merryweather hurried **out** to look for the prince. He was the only one who could break the spell. He was a prisoner in Maleficent's castle. They set him free. He wanted to **help**. The good fairies gave him the Shield of Virtue and the Sword of Truth. Maleficent's castle was well-guarded, but the good fairies found **their** way out.

He got out with their help.

Maleficent did not want the prince to kiss Aurora. She tried to stop him. She made thorny bushes grow **up** in his path. **He** cut right through them with his sword.

Then she turned herself into a dragon. She stood in the prince's path. She **did not give** him a chance to get around her.

He did not give up.

The dragon charged toward the prince. **It** breathed fire. There were flames all around. The prince's horse **saw** the flames. It was afraid. It ran away. **Then** the prince was out on the edge of a cliff. **He** had nowhere to go, but he could not **fall**. He had to save Aurora. He threw his enchanted sword into the dragon's heart. The dragon roared in pain.

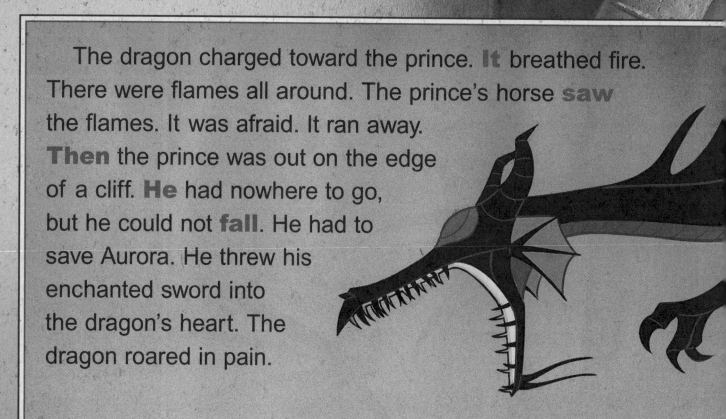

Then he saw it fall.

Prince Phillip raced back to the castle. He found Aurora's room. He bent down and kissed her. She woke up, and so **did** everyone else.

That night there was a ball. Aurora and the prince danced for a long time. The two fathers watched for a while. Then **they** started to plan a royal wedding.

Everyone wanted Aurora and Prince Phillip to live happily ever after.

They did.

Say the word at the top of each box. Then fill in the missing letters.

oh

oh

Oh

no

no

no

she

she

she

said

said

said

Trace the name with your pencil. Then write the name on your own.

 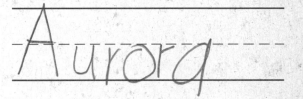

Say the word at the top of each box. Then fill in the missing letters.

she

she

she

told

told

told

them

them

them

Say the word at the top of each box. Then fill in the missing letters.

he	said
h__ __	__ __ s __ __ __ d
__ __ e	__ ai __

Read the words in the box. Then read the sentences. Find the word in the box that correctly completes each sentence. Write the word on the line.

_____

Aurora said she _____ come.

_____

She had to _____.

_____

_____ told them to go away.

_____

He _____ he would go.

He
would
said
come

Read the words in the box. Then read the sentences. Find the word in the box that correctly completes each sentence. Write the word on the line.

She had to go _____.

He said _____ go back.

_____ would go back.

Aurora had to _____.

He _____ to take Aurora away.

| had |
| to |
| She |
| back |
| go |

Say the word at the top of each box. Then fill in the missing letters.

they	to
___ ___ ey	t ___
th ___	___ o

had	him
h ___ d	___ im
___ a ___	h ___

	find
	___ i ___
	f ___ nd

30

Read the words in the box. Then read the sentences. Find the word in the box that correctly completes each sentence. Write the word on the line.

_____ _____ them.

_____ _____ would help them.

_____ He _____ away.

_____ He had _____ help.

_____ He would find _____ .

_____ He would go _____ them.

out

their

Help

with

He

got

Say the word at the top of each box. Then fill in the missing letters.

give

___ ___ ve

gi ___ ___

not

n ___ t

___ o ___

did

d ___ d

___ i ___

he

___ ___ e

h ___ ___

up

___ p

u ___

32

Say the word at the top of each box. Then fill in the missing letters.

then	saw
th _ _ _	s _ w
_ _ en	_ a _

Read the words in the box. Then read the sentences. Find the word in the box that correctly completes each sentence. Write the word on the line.

_____

She saw it _____ .

He would take _____ .

She _____ it.

_____ she saw them.

Then
it
fall
saw

Say the word at the top of each box. Then fill in the missing letters.

they	did
th_ _ _ _ _ _ey	d_d _ _i_

Read the words in the box. Then read the sentences. Find the word in the box that correctly completes each sentence. Write the word on the line.

did
They

They _____ not take Aurora.

_____ did not come.

Aurora

away

back

come

did

fall

find

give

go

got

had

he

help

him

it

no

not

oh

out

said

saw

she

take

their

them

then

they

to

told

up

with

would

Adapted by Linda Armstrong

Table of Contents

Once there was a girl named Belle. She loved to read and dream. A hunter named Gaston wanted to marry her, but she did not like him. She dreamed of meeting a handsome prince.

Belle's father was an inventor. He was always trying to **make** things.

One day her father showed Belle a wonderful new invention. "I will take **it** to the fair tomorrow," he said.

"I know **you will** win first prize," **Belle said**.

Just then there was a big BOOM. It came from the invention.

"It just needs a little more **work**," her father said.

"You will make it work," Belle said.

Her father worked hard to fix his invention. The next day it was ready. He put it in the cart. He hitched up the horse. Then he started off for the fair. He did not make it. He got lost in the woods. There were wild animals. The horse was afraid of them. **It** threw the old man off of its back. Then it **ran** away with the cart. The horse knew where **home** was.

It ran home.

Belle found the horse and cart. Her father **was** not with them.

"You must take me to Papa," she said to the horse.

She climbed up on its back. Thick fog filled the woods, but **it** did not stop her. She could not see **very** well, but she rode on. **Big** bats flew down and wild animals growled all around, but she rode on. At last she saw a castle.

It was very big.

Belle went into the castle. Her father was locked up.

"Oh, Papa!" Belle said. She gave him a big hug.

An ugly Beast in a royal cape appeared. "I found this man in my castle," the Beast said. "Now he is my prisoner."

"Please **let him go**. I will stay in his place," Belle said.

The Beast made Belle promise to stay with him forever. Then he took her father to the gate.

The Beast let him go.

The Beast led **Belle** to her room.

After the Beast left, Belle was amazed to find out that **his** teapot, clock, and cup could talk. They told her they used to **be** servants at the castle. **All** of them had been put under a spell. Belle was glad to have friends, but she was still sad.

Meanwhile Belle's father ran back to town. He told everyone about the Beast. But nobody believed him. So Belle's father set out to rescue her himself. Gaston wanted to rescue **Belle**. If he saved her, she **would** have to marry him.

Belle would be his after all.

Over time **Belle** learned that the Beast was not really mean. He was gentle and sweet. One night she danced with him. Then Belle told the Beast that she missed her father. She **had to** go home. The Beast did not **stop** her.

Back at home, Belle took care of her father. Gaston came to visit **them**. He asked Belle to marry him. She said no. Gaston got angry. He could tell that Belle's heart belonged to the Beast. He convinced the villagers that the Beast was dangerous.

He led an angry mob to the castle.

Belle had to stop them.

Belle and her father rode through the woods as fast as they could. Belle did not want anyone to get **hurt**. When they got to the castle, Belle saw Gaston and the Beast. They were out on a high balcony. Gaston **was** raising his bow. **He** shot the Beast with an arrow.

Belle started crying. She ran up the stairs.

He was hurt.

The Beast saw Belle standing **there**. He picked Gaston up by the neck.

"Let me go!" said Gaston.

The Beast put Gaston down and told him to go.

Gaston did **not** go. He stabbed **the Beast** in the back. The Beast roared in pain. Gaston stepped back. He slipped and fell off the balcony.

The Beast lay in Belle's arms. He **was** dying. "You came back," he said. "I got to see you once more."

"No! Do not die," said Belle. "I love you."

Then something strange and wonderful happened.

The Beast was not there.

In his place stood a handsome prince. The Beast had been a prince all the time, but he was under a spell. When he loved Belle and she loved him, the spell was broken. The Beast became a prince again and all the enchanted things in the castle turned back into servants.

Belle and the Prince danced together.

"I am so happy," **said** the Prince.

"So am I," said Belle.

ACTIVITY 1

Say the word at the top of each box. Then fill in the missing letters.

will	make
wi__ __	m__k__
__ __ll	__a__e
you	**work**
y__ __	__ __rk
__ou	wo__ __
said	
__ai__	
s__ __d	

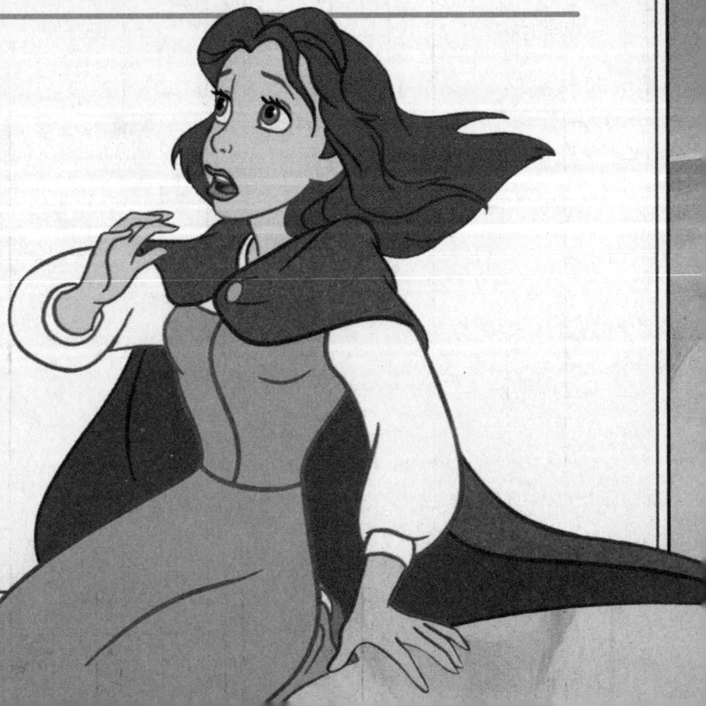

Say the word at the top of each box. Then fill in the missing letters.

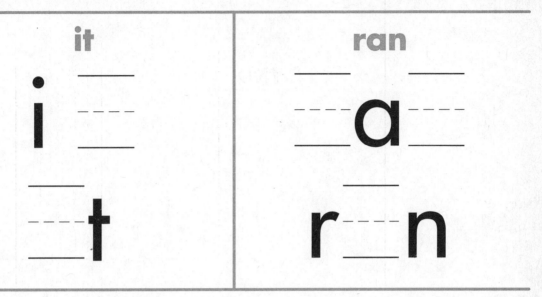

it	ran
i	a
t	r_n

Read the words in the box. Then read the sentences. Find the word in the box that correctly completes each sentence. Write the word on the line.

_____

Belle _____ home.

_____

_____ ran.

| It |
| home |
| ran |

_____

He will go _____.

Say the word at the top of each box. Then fill in the missing letters.

very	big
__ __ __	__ __ __
__ __ ry	__ __ g
__ __ __	__ __ __
ve __ __ __	b __ __ __

Read the words in the box. Then read the sentences. Find the word in the box that correctly completes each sentence. Write the word on the line.

It _____ big.

He was not _____ big.

You said it was _____.

Was _____ big?

very

was

big

it

Read the words in the box. Then read the sentences. Find the word in the box that correctly completes each sentence. Write the word on the line.

_____

Belle_____ him go.

_____

The Beast will_____ home.

_____

Let_____ go!

him
let
go

Trace the name with your pencil. Then write the name on your own.

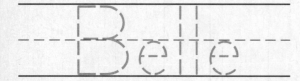

Say the word at the top of each box. Then fill in the missing letters.

would

w _ _ _ ld

wou _ _ _

be

b _ _

_ _ e

his

h _ s

_ i _

Read the words in the box. Then read the sentences. Find the word in the box that correctly completes each sentence. Write the word on the line.

_____

He will stop _____.

_____

_____ them!

_____

He _____ to stop.

_____

He had _____ go home.

had
to
Stop
them

Say the word at the top of each box. Then fill in the missing letters.

hurt

hu_ _ _

_ _ur_ _

was

w_ _s

_ _a_ _

Read the words in the box. Then read the sentences. Find the word in the box that correctly completes each sentence. Write the word on the line.

_____

_____ will not be hurt.

He _____ hurt.

Belle will be _____ .

He

hurt

was

Read the words in the box. Then read the sentences. Find the word in the box that correctly completes each sentence. Write the word on the line.

_____

It was _____ his.

_____

_____ he was.

_____

The Beast _____ not at home.

_____

_____ Beast was big.

| not |
| There |
| The |
| was |

Say the word at the top of each box. Then fill in the missing letters.

so	am
__ o __ s ____	a ____ ____ m

said	Belle
____ ai ____ ____ d	B __ lle Be ____ e

after

all

am

be

Belle

big

go

had

he

him

his

home

hurt

I

it

let

make

not

ran

said

so

stop

The Beast

them

there

to

very

was

will

work

would

you

Disney's Aladdin

Adapted by Linda Armstrong

Table of Contents

"Get him, Rajah!" Princess Jasmine shouted. "I want to see him **run**."

The surprised prince raced away from her pet tiger, but he was not fast enough. When Rajah took a big bite out of his pants, Princess Jasmine laughed.

"It is not funny," said Jasmine's father, the Sultan. "You must marry a prince before your next birthday. It is the law."

"That law is not fair," Jasmine said. **She wanted to** marry for love.

The next day, Princess Jasmine put her fine clothes **away**. In disguise, she climbed over the palace wall.

She wanted to run away.

Princess Jasmine visited the marketplace. She chose a fine apple from one of the stands. **She** handed it to a hungry child.

"Where is my money?" the apple seller demanded.

Jasmine **could not** pay him.

When she started to leave, he put out his hand to **stop** her. "If you take my apples, you must pay for **them**," he said. "If you cannot pay, you are a thief."

Jasmine was terrified. She did not know what to do. Then a handsome young man appeared. He helped her get away. He led her through narrow streets to safety. The two of them laughed and talked at his rooftop home. Suddenly palace guards broke in. They grabbed him.

"Let him go," Jasmine ordered. "I am the princess."

"I am sorry. These orders come from Jafar," the guard said. Jasmine knew that the Sultan's advisor was very powerful. The guards arrested her new friend.

She could not stop them.

Jasmine's new friend, Aladdin, and his pet monkey, Abu, sat in the palace dungeon. Another prisoner said he needed Aladdin's help to get a great treasure. When Aladdin agreed to help, the old man pushed on a stone, and a door opened up. The old man led Aladdin to a cave in the desert.

"Who disturbs my slumber?" the cave asked.

"It is I, Aladdin," Aladdin said.

"Proceed. Touch nothing but the lamp," said the cave.

"Fetch me the lamp," said the old man. "Then you shall have your reward."

In the cave, Aladdin and Abu met a Magic Carpet. It followed them through rooms filled with treasure. At last Aladdin found the lamp. Unfortunately, Abu **could not** resist a huge ruby. When he touched it, the whole cave started to shake. **They** rode the Magic Carpet to the cave entrance, which was starting to close. Aladdin climbed up and handed the old man the lamp. Instead of rewarding Aladdin, the old man tried to stab him. When Abu bit the attacker's wrist, the old man dropped Aladdin and Abu back into the cave, but not before Abu grabbed the lamp. The entrance closed over them. They tried to get out.

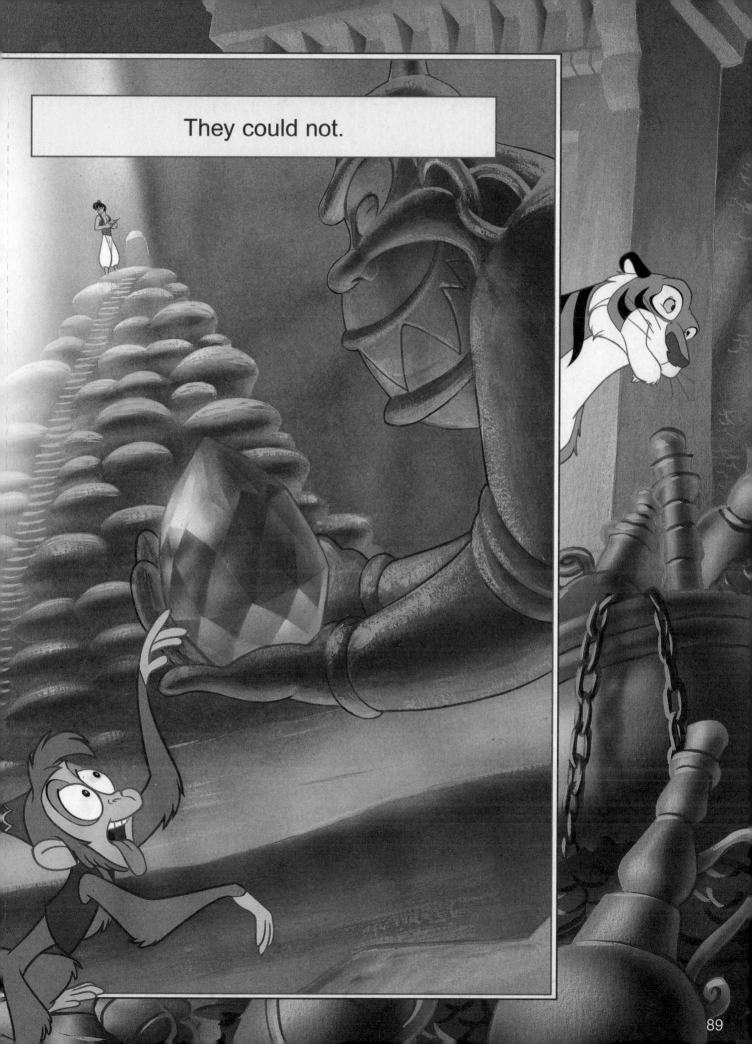

They could not.

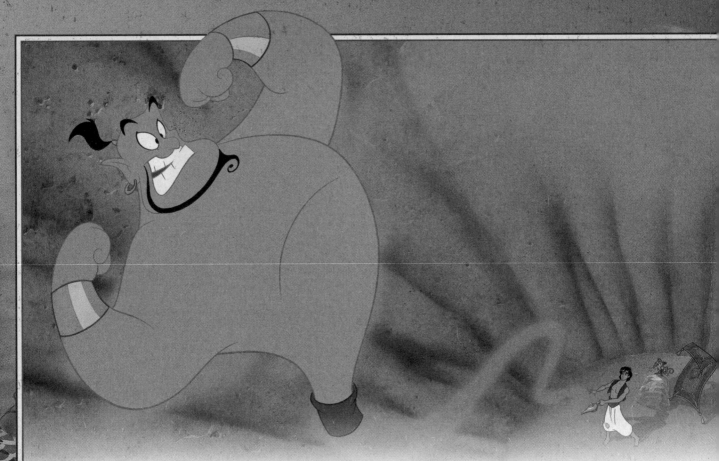

Aladdin sat on the cave floor staring at the battered, old lamp. He wondered why the old man wanted **it**. The cave had so many real treasures. Aladdin rubbed the dusty lamp.

Poof! A big, blue Genie came out of the lamp.

"What is your first wish, Master?" the Genie asked.

"What do you mean?" Aladdin asked.

"I am the Genie of the lamp. You are my master. I will grant you three wishes. Just say what you want," the Genie said.

Aladdin did not believe him. "Some Genie. He cannot even get us out of here," he said.

"Excuse me?" said the Genie. He called the Magic Carpet, and they all climbed on. The Genie opened up a crack in the cave. Then they sailed out into the open air.

Aladdin thought about what to wish for next. There was only one thing he really wanted.

"I want to be a prince so I can marry Jasmine," he **said**.

"**Is** that your wish?" the Genie asked.

"It is," Aladdin said.

As soon as he made the wish, Aladdin became Prince Ali.

The Genie wanted to **show** everyone how important Aladdin was, so he created a huge parade. Aladdin rode on the back of an elephant and tossed gold coins to the crowd.

After the parade, Aladdin went to see Princess Jasmine, but she thought he was just another spoiled prince. She would not **let** him stay.

Later that night, he rode up to her balcony on the Magic Carpet. "Princess Jasmine?" **he** called.

"Who is there?" she asked.

"Prince Ali," he said. She came closer and looked deep into his eyes.

"**You** remind **me** of someone," she **said**.

"Would you like to ride on the Magic Carpet?" he asked.

"How does it work?" she asked.

"Let me show you," he said.

Aladdin and Jasmine soared out over the city. When they returned, Jasmine was in love.

Jafar saw **it** all. **He** called the palace guards. "Get rid of that prince," he ordered.

The guards **took** Aladdin and threw him over a cliff into the ocean.

At that very moment Jasmine went **to** see her father. "I want to marry Prince Ali," she said.

"What excellent news," her father said.

"That is impossible. Prince Ali is gone," said Jafar.

"No, I am not gone. I am here," Aladdin said. The Genie had saved him.

Jafar swept out of the room, but not before he spotted the lamp hidden in Aladdin's robe.

Later that night, **Jafar** tricked Aladdin into leaving his room. Jafar's parrot flew into the room and found the lamp.

He took it to Jafar.

When Jafar rubbed the lamp, he became the master. Now, the Genie had to **work** for him.

"Make me into the Sultan," he ordered. Then he became the Sultan, but it was not enough.

"Make me into the most powerful sorcerer in the world," Jafar ordered, and he was. He used his new magical powers to send Aladdin off to a land of snow and ice.

But it was still not enough for Jafar.

"Make Jasmine fall in love with me," he ordered.

"Uh, boss, I cannot do that," said the Genie, but Jafar **did not** listen.

Meanwhile, the Magic Carpet carried Aladdin back to the palace. Jasmine saw him hiding behind a column. He was waiting for the right time to come out. The Genie could not make anyone fall in love, but Jasmine had a **plan**. She pretended **that** she was in love with Jafar.

That plan did not work.

Jasmine pulled Jafar in to kiss him. Then he saw Aladdin's reflection in her shiny crown.

"I **think** you have betrayed me," Jafar said. "And now you will pay."

He cast a spell that trapped Jasmine inside a huge hourglass. Sand poured down all around her. **Aladdin had to** do something **fast**, or Jasmine would be buried alive.

When Aladdin tried to stab Jafar, the sorcerer changed himself into a huge snake. The snake knocked the sword out of Aladdin's hands. Its coils tightened around him.

Aladdin had to think fast.

"You are powerful, but not as powerful as the Genie," he said.

Jafar, the snake, loosened his coils. "You are right," he said. "Genie, **I** am ready to make my third wish. I wish to be an all-powerful Genie."

The Genie raised his arms.

The snake began to change. Jafar the Genie grew and grew until he filled the room. "Oh, what amazing power," he said. **Then** he screamed. The lamp sucked him down inside.

"Great big powers, itty bitty living space," Aladdin said.

When Jafar was gone, **Aladdin** smashed the hourglass and saved **Jasmine**.

Finally, Aladdin faced Jasmine and her father. "I have something to tell you," he **said**. "I am not really Prince Ali. I am just Aladdin. I cannot marry the princess."

"I think my daughter was right about that law," the Sultan said. "It was not fair. Jasmine may **pick** anyone she wants to be her husband."

"Then I pick Aladdin," Jasmine said.

Say the word at the top of each box. Then fill in the missing letters.

run	away
r u n	a way
r u n	aw a y

Read the words in the box. Then read the sentences. Find the word in the box that correctly completes each sentence. Write the word on the line.

_____

She could _____ fast.

_____ wanted to run.

She did not run _____.

She _____ to run.

wanted

She

away

run

Say the word at the top of each box. Then fill in the missing letters.

could

cou _ _ _

c _ _ ld

not

n _ t

_ _ o _

stop

_ _ op

st _ _ _

them

_ _ em

th _ _ _

103

Say the word at the top of each box. Then fill in the missing letters.

they	could
th___ ___ey	c___ld cou___

Read the words in the box. Then read the sentences. Find the word in the box that correctly completes each sentence. Write the word on the line.

They
not
could

_____ did not run.

They did _____ show it to him.

They _____ not work.

Trace the name with your pencil. Then write the name on your own.

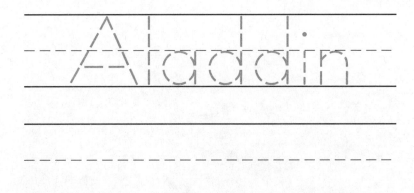

Read the words in the box. Then read the sentences. Find the word in the box that correctly completes each sentence. Write the word on the line.

_____

Aladdin _____ to run.

is
it
said

It _____ Aladdin.

Aladdin said to stop _____.

ACTIVITY 5

Read the words in the box. Then read the sentences. Find the word in the box that correctly completes each sentence. Write the word on the line.

He could not stop _____.

_____ let me run away.

He did not _____ me stop.

He wanted to _____ me.

show
He
me
let

Trace the name with your pencil. Then write the name on your own.

Say the word at the top of each box. Then fill in the missing letters.

he	took
h___	___ oo ___
___ e	t ___ k

it

___ t

i ___

Read the words in the box. Then read the sentences. Find the word in the box that correctly completes each sentence. Write the word on the line.

_____

_____ did not work.

Jafar's plan did not _____.

That is _____ work.

He _____ not run.

work
did
That
not

Say the word at the top of each box. Then fill in the missing letters.

think	fast
th__nk	f__st
thi____	fa_____

Read the words in the box. Then read the sentences. Find the word in the box that correctly completes each sentence. Write the word on the line.

_____

Aladdin had to _____.

_____

He wanted to run _____.

He had _____ show them.

Aladdin _____ to stop.

| had |
| think |
| fast |
| to |

Trace the name with your pencil. Then write the name on your own.

Say the word at the top of each box. Then fill in the missing letters.

then

___ ___ ___

___ ___ en

th ___ ___

pick

p ___ ck

pi ___

I

Aladdin

away

could

did

fast

had

he

I

is

it

Jafar

Jasmine

let

me

not

pick

plan

run

said

she

show

stop

that

them

then

they

think

to

took

wanted

work

you

Walt Disney's

Snow White
and the Seven Dwarfs

Adapted by Linda Armstrong

Walt Disney's

Snow White
and the Seven Dwarfs

Table of Contents

There once was a princess named Snow White. **She** lived in a palace with her mean stepmother, the Queen. The Queen was proud **to** be the most beautiful woman in the kingdom. Every day she stood in front of a Magic Mirror.

"Magic Mirror on the wall, who is the fairest one of all?" she asked. The Mirror always **gave** the same answer, "You are."

Then one day it gave a different answer. **It** said Snow White was the most beautiful.

The Queen was very angry. She called her Huntsman. She held out a box to **him**.

"You must take Snow White into the forest and do away with her. Put her heart in this box and bring it back to me," she said.

She gave it to him.

The Huntsman told **Snow White** that the Queen wanted her to pick some wildflowers for the table. The princess sang as she went into the woods with him. She **ran** here and there to pick flowers. Even if it meant giving up his own life, the Huntsman realized that he could not hurt her.

Kneeling down before her he said, "Princess, the Queen is jealous of your beauty. She wanted me to kill you. You must run away. You must never come back."

Snow White ran.

Alone in the woods, Snow White was frightened. She started to cry. Birds and animals came out to see her. She felt better when she saw **them**.

"Is there a place where I could sleep?" she asked.

They led her to a little house in a clearing. **There** was no one home, but the sink was full **of** dirty dishes. There were **seven** little chairs and seven little beds. Snow White thought seven children lived in the house.

"Poor little things, they must not have a mother," she said.

Snow White liked to help. She swept and dusted, washed and scrubbed until everything was clean. Then she went upstairs and fell asleep.

When she woke up, a lot of little men **were** staring at her.

There were seven of them.

She told them dinner **was** almost ready. They would have to wash their hands before they ate. Every **one** of the Seven Dwarfs did. The soup smelled **good**, and they were very hungry. After they ate, they sang and danced. Then Snow White told **a** story. **It** was about the prince of her dreams.

It was a good one.

In her room at the palace, the Queen asked, "Magic Mirror on the wall, who is the fairest one of all?"

The Mirror said Snow White **was** still alive. That made the Queen very angry.

She mixed up a pot of poison. She dipped a **pretty red** apple into **it**. She put the poisoned apple in a basket. Then the wicked Queen dressed up as an old peddler woman **and** set off for the woods to find Snow White.

After the Seven Dwarfs went to work, the wicked Queen went to the window of their house. Snow White was busy making pies. The wicked Queen pretended to be selling apples. She said that apple pies were the best. She asked Snow White to taste one of her apples.

The Queen held out the poisoned apple.

It was pretty and red.

Snow White took just one bite of the apple. **After** that she fell to the floor.

Snow White's animal friends had seen the old woman coming. They did not trust her. They **went** to get the Seven Dwarfs. The Dwarfs ran fast as they could. **They** got to the house just as the wicked Queen was leaving. They saw **her** running away.

They went after her.

The Dwarfs chased the Queen through the woods. **They saw her** running between the trees, but they **never** got close. Rain poured down. **Again** and again thunder rolled across the sky. The Seven Dwarfs chased the wicked Queen out onto a high, narrow ledge. Lightning hit the cliff. It broke the rock where the Queen was standing. Down she fell.

They never saw her again.

When the Dwarfs **came back** home, they found **Snow White**. She was still beautiful. She seemed to be asleep. They did not want **to** put her under the ground. They made a bed of gold for her. They put it in the woods.

Soon the Prince of a nearby kingdom heard about the girl in the forest. He came to see her for himself. The moment he did, he fell in love. She was the most beautiful girl he had seen in his **life**. When he bent down and kissed Snow White, the wicked Queen's spell was broken.

Snow White came back to life.

Snow White was very happy. She had dreamed this handsome prince **would ride** into her life. She knew the two of them would be **together** always. She thanked the Seven Dwarfs for their help. She kissed every one of them. **They** waved good-bye. Then Snow White got on the Prince's white horse.

They would ride together.

Say the word at the top of each box. Then fill in the missing letters.

she

_ _ _ _ _ e

sh_ _

gave

g _ v _

_ a _ e

it

_ t

i_

to

_ o

t _

him

_ i _

h _ m

140

Trace the name with your pencil. Then write the name on your own.

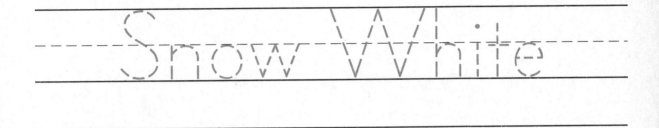

Say the word below. Then fill in the missing letters.

ran

r __ n   __ a __

Say the word at the top of each box. Then fill in the missing letters.

there

_ _ _ _
_ _ _ ere
th_r_

were

_ _ _ _
_ _ _re
we_ _ _

seven

_ _ _ _
_e_e
s_v_n

of

_ _
o
_f

them

_ _ _
_ _ em
th_ _ _

ACTIVITY 4

Trace the word with your pencil. Then write the word on your own.

_____   _____

---------- ----------   ----------------------------

_____   _____

_____

Say the word at the top of each box. Then fill in the missing letters.

it

__t

i_

was

w__s

__a__

good

g__d

__oo__

Read the words in the box. Then read the sentences. Find the word in the box that correctly completes each sentence. Write the word on the line.

_____

_____ was pretty.

Snow White was _____.

She _____ good!

It was red _____ pretty.

It was a pretty _____ one.

and	
was	
It	
pretty	
red	

Say the word at the top of each box. Then fill in the missing letters.

went

we___
___nt

after

___ft___r
a___e

Read the words in the box. Then read the sentences. Find the word in the box that correctly completes each sentence. Write the word on the line.

_____

They ran _____ her.

They saw _____.

_____ came back.

They never_____there again.

her

went

after

They

145

ACTIVITY 7

Say the word at the top of each box. Then fill in the missing letters.

they

t _ _ y
_ he _

never

n _ v _ r
_ e _ e _

saw

_ a _
s _ w

her

h _ _
_ _ r

146

Read the words in the box. Then read the sentences. Find the word in the box that correctly completes each sentence. Write the word on the line.

_____

They came _____ her.

_____

They _____ back.

_____

They ran _____ to him.

_____

She came back to _____.

_____

Her life _____ good.

life
was
back
came
to

Say the word at the top of each box. Then fill in the missing letters.

they	**ride**
__ __ __	__ __ __ __
__ __ ey	r __ d __
t __ e __	__ i __ e

Read the words in the box. Then read the sentences. Find the word in the box that correctly completes each sentence. Write the word on the line.

_____

They came _____ her.

_____

They _____ ride after her.

_____

They ran _____ to her.

_____

She came back to _____.

life
to
would
back

148

a

after

again

and

back

came

gave

good

her

him

it

life

never

of

one

pretty

ran

red

ride

saw

seven

she

Snow White

them

there

they

to

together

was

went

were

would

Disney's

THE LITTLE
MERMAID

Adapted by Linda Armstrong

Disney's

THE LITTLE MERMAID

Table of Contents

Once there was a little mermaid named **Ariel**. She was tired of living under the sea **with** her father. Sometimes she swam up **to** the top of the water, even though her father did not like her to. Ariel wondered about the world above the sea.

"**I** love new things. I **want** to see more of **them**," Ariel **said**.

The land looked like a good place to **be**. Human beings lived there.

"I want to be with them," Ariel said.

One day **Ariel** saw a new ship. She swam up **to** it as fast as she could. A young human was on the ship. Ariel **thought** he was handsome. Some of his friends were having a birthday party **for** him.

The man was **Prince Eric**.

"We **want** to celebrate with you," his friends said. Then, they started to **sing** and dance.

One man asked the prince when he would find a girl to marry. "**I** just haven't found her," the prince said.

I want to sing for Prince Eric, Ariel thought.

Just then, a storm came up. Big waves tossed the ship from side **to** side. Prince Eric fell into the water.

Ariel pulled him to the shore. While he was asleep on the beach, she sang to **him**. **She** left before he could **see** her.

When her father, King Triton, found out what Ariel **had** done, he was very angry. He told her to stay away from human beings, but Ariel loved Prince Eric.

She had to see him.

The evil sea witch, Ursula, was the only one who could help. Ariel went to see her.

"**I know** what you want," Ursula said. "**I will** make you human if you give me your voice."

Ariel thought about it.

"Oh, and one more thing," said Ursula. "If **Prince Eric** does not kiss you in three days, you are mine!"

166

I know Prince Eric will, Ariel thought.

"So, **will** you give me your voice?" Ursula asked.

"Yes, **I** will," Ariel **said**.

As soon as she spoke, Ariel had human legs. She could not swim. Her friends had to **help** her to shore.

When Prince Eric found Ariel, **he** did not know who she was.

"Can you speak?" he asked.

She shook her head.

"I will help," he said.

The next day, Prince Eric showed her around the kingdom. They **went** for a boat ride. Eric leaned **over** to kiss Ariel. The evil Ursula sent her pet eels out to the boat. The two eels swam around the boat. They swam under it. The eels were big and the **boat** was small.

The boat went over.

On the third day, Ursula changed herself into a pretty girl. The girl **had** Ariel's voice in a shell. She wore the shell on a ribbon around her neck.

When Prince Eric heard that voice, he forgot all about the real **Ariel**. He could not **help** himself. He asked the girl to marry him.

Ariel's sea friends found out what Ursula had done. **They** all went up **to** the ship.

They had to help Ariel.

There was a fight. The shell broke. Ariel could speak again. She told Prince Eric who she was. **He** did **not** have time to kiss her before the sun went down.

Ariel turned back into a mermaid. The evil Ursula took Ariel down into the sea. An old ship appeared in the battle that followed. Prince Eric jumped on the ship and fought Ursula. He saved Ariel. But Prince Eric **could** not stay in the sea with her. He had to breathe air to **live**.

He could not live there.

Ariel was safe under the sea, but she was not **happy**. She and Prince Eric could never be **together**.

Her father, King Triton, loved Ariel very much. He did not want her to be sad. He made Ariel human again.

Prince Eric was very glad to see her. **They were** married right away.

They were happy together.

Say the word at the top of each box. Then fill in the missing letters.

want

wa _ _ _

_ _ ant

to

_ _ o

t _

be

b _ _

_ e

them

_ _ em

th _ _

said

s _ _ d

_ d

Trace the name with your pencil. Then write the name on your own.

Prince Eric

Read the words in the box. Then read the sentences. Find the word in the box that correctly completes each sentence. Write the word on the line.

I want to _____.

" ___

_____ like Prince Eric," said Ariel.

I like them, _____ Ariel.

Ariel will sing _____ Prince Eric.

| thought |
| I |
| sing |
| for |

179

Say the word at the top of each box. Then fill in the missing letters.

she

_ _ _ _ _ _
_ _ _ _ _ e
_ _ _ _ _ _
s _ _ _ _ _

to

_ _ _ _ _ _
_ _ _ _ o _
_ _ _ _ _ _
t _ _ _ _ _

see

_ _ _ _ _ _
s _ _ _ _ _
_ _ _ _ _ _
e _ _ _ _ _

had

_ _ _ _ _ _
_ _ _ a _ _
_ _ _ _ _ _
h _ _ _ _ _

him

_ _ _ _ _ _
h _ _ _ _ _
_ _ _ _ _ _
_ _ _ m _ _

Read the words in the box. Then read the sentences. Find the word in the box that correctly completes each sentence. Write the word on the line.

thought	Ariel	I
know	will	He

_____ want to sing.

I _____ Ariel.

_____ will sing for Ariel.

Ariel _____ sing for him.

I like to sing, Ariel _____.

"I know Prince Eric," _____ said.

181

Say the word at the top of each box. Then fill in the missing letters.

will

wi____
____ il

help

h____ p
____ el____

I

____
____
____

he

h____
____ e

said

____ aid
s____ d

182

Say the word at the top of each box. Then fill in the missing letters.

over

___
___ ver

ov___

boat

_____ t

b___ t

Read the words in the box. Then read the sentences. Find the word in the box that correctly completes each sentence. Write the word on the line.

_____

She went _____ there.

_____

He was in the _____.

_____

Where was _____ boat?

_____

He _____ over there.

boat

the

over

went

ACTIVITY 7

Trace the name with your pencil. Then write the name on your own.

Say the word at the top of each box. Then fill in the missing letters.

help

_ elp

h _ p

they

_ ey

t _ y

had

h _ d

_ d

ACTIVITY 8

Read the words in the box. Then read the sentences. Find the word in the box that correctly completes each sentence. Write the word on the line.

Prince Eric _____ not live there.

He did not _____ there.

Did _____ live there?

He is over _____.

He did _____ sing to Ariel.

could

not

there

live

he

185

Say the word at the top of each box. Then fill in the missing letters.

were

w_ _ _ _ r

w_ _ _ _ _ r

_ _ _ _ ere

happy

ha_ _ _ y

_ _ _ _ pp

they

_ _ _ _ _

_ _ _ _ _ y

th_ _ _

Prince Eric

© Disney

Ariel

© Disney

for

© Disney

they

© Disney

boat

© Disney

be

© Disney

want

© Disney

sing

© Disney

she

he

I

to

live

were

help

with

said

© Disney

see

© Disney

them

© Disney

there

© Disney

will

© Disney

together

© Disney

went

over

© Disney

© Disney

know

thought

the

him

had

could

not

happy

Walt Disney's
Cinderella

Adapted by Linda Armstrong

WALT DISNEY'S

Cinderella

Table of Contents

Once there was a kind and gentle girl named
Cinderella. Everyone loved her, even the mice in
the hall and the birds in the garden.

Her widowed father thought Cinderella should have a
mother, so he married again. His new wife had two girls just
Cinderella's age.

Cinderella's stepmother pretended to be kind, but she was
lazy and mean. When Cinderella's father died, her
stepmother did not want **to do** any **work**. Her stepsisters
were mean and lazy, too. Poor Cinderella **had** to do **all** of
the cooking, sewing, and cleaning.

Cinderella had to do all the work.

One day, Cinderella was sweeping. **She** heard a knock on the door. She **did not** know who it could be.

"**Open** in the name of the King!" someone called.

She hurried to the door. **It** was a messenger. He gave her a big white envelope. It had the royal seal.

She did not open it.

Cinderella took the letter to her stepmother. It said that every maiden in the kingdom was invited to a ball.

"That means I can **go**, too," said Cinderella.

The mean Stepmother said Cinderella **could** go IF she finished her work.

"Oh, and of course you will need a ball gown," she added. She thought Cinderella would **not** be able to find one.

Cinderella did find a gown. It had been her mother's. It was pretty, but old. While Cinderella was finishing her work, the birds and the mice fixed the dress. They used sashes and ribbons the stepsisters had thrown away.

When her stepsisters saw Cinderella's gown, they were angry. They tore off the sashes. The gown was ruined.

Cinderella could not go.

Cinderella did not know what to do. She sat down in the garden and cried. Her Fairy Godmother came to help. **She** waved her wand. A pumpkin became a fine coach. Cinderella's mouse friends became four white horses.

Next, the Fairy Godmother changed Cinderella's torn dress into a ball gown. Cinderella's old shoes became sparkling glass slippers. The Fairy Godmother **said** the spell would end at the last stroke of twelve. Everything **would** change back into what it had been before. She told Cinderella she had to be back before midnight.

Cinderella said she would.

The Prince **did not** like any of the girls **he** met at the ball. Then he saw Cinderella.

He walked right by the stepsisters, **who** were bowing to him. They did not even **know** he **was** gone.

He asked Cinderella to dance. **She** said yes.

She did not know who he was.

They danced and danced. Cinderella was very happy. Then she heard the clock chime. It was the first stroke of midnight.

"I must go," she said.

She ran out the door and down the steps. One of her glass slippers fell off. She could not go back for it. The Prince and the Grand Duke ran after her. The Grand Duke **got** the slipper.

Cinderella's coach was waiting **in** front of the palace.

She got in.

When the clock struck twelve, the spell was broken. The coach, horses, and ball gown were gone, but Cinderella still had her glass slipper. **She** also had happy memories of the ball.

The Prince did not know Cinderella's name. The slipper she had lost was his only clue. He promised to marry the girl whose foot fit the shoe. The mean Stepmother told her daughters about the slipper.

"**It** is sure to fit **one of you**," she **said**.

The stepsisters looked at their big bare feet. They looked at each other. Then they began to fight.

"It **will** not **be** you! The slipper will fit me!" each one said.

The Stepmother held up her hand.

"It will be one of you," she said.

When the Grand Duke **came** to the house, the stepsisters were very excited. Each of them tried on the slipper, but it did not fit. It was too small.

The wicked Stepmother had locked **Cinderella** up in her room, but she got out. She came to the top of the stairs. She asked to try on the slipper.

"Yes, come **down**. Every maiden must try on the slipper," the Grand Duke said.

Cinderella came down.

Cinderella slipped her foot into the glass slipper. It fit perfectly. She had **always** known it would.

The mean Stepmother and her spoiled daughters **were** very angry. Cinderella and the Grand Duke went to the palace **together**.

The Prince was very happy to see Cinderella again. Soon **they** were married.

They were together always.

Say the word at the top of each box. Then fill in the missing letters.

had

h _ _ d

_ _ _ a _

to

_ _ o

t _

do

d _ _ _

_ _ _ o _

work

_ _ o k

wo _ _ _

all

a _ _ _

_ _ _ ll

Read the words in the box. Then read the sentences. Find the word in the box that correctly completes each sentence. Write the word on the line.

She had to _____ it.

She had to do _____.

She _____ not do it.

Did _____ open it?

She did _____ open it.

she

it

did

open

not

Say the word at the top of each box. Then fill in the missing letters.

could	not
c___ld	n__t
___ou___	___o___

Read the words in the box. Then read the sentences. Find the word in the box that correctly completes each sentence. Write the word on the line.

_____

She could not _____.

_____

She could _____ work.

could

not

go

_____

She _____ not do the work.

Say the word at the top of each box. Then fill in the missing letters.

would	she
w___ld	sh__
___ou__	___e

Read the words in the box. Then read the sentences. Find the word in the box that correctly completes each sentence. Write the word on the line.

would
She
said

She_____she would do it.

She_____open it.

_____would do all the work.

219

Say the word at the top of each box. Then fill in the missing letters.

she	not
___ ___ e	___ n ___ t
s ___ ___	___ o ___

did	know
d ___ d	___ ___ ow
d ___ ___	kn ___ ___

he

h ___

___ e

Say the word at the top of each box. Then fill in the missing letters.

in	got
__ n	g __ t
i __	__ t

Read the words in the box. Then read the sentences. Find the word in the box that correctly completes each sentence. Write the word on the line.

_____

She _____ it.

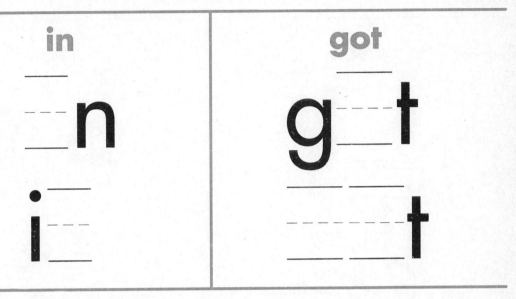

_____

Cinderella got _____.

_____

_____ could not go in.

got
in
She

Say the word at the top of each box. Then fill in the missing letters.

it

_t

i_

be

b_

_e

will

wi__

__ll

one

o_e

_n_

you

y__

__ou

of

o_

__f

ACTIVITY 8

Say the word at the top of each box. Then fill in the missing letters.

came	down
c __ m __	d __ __ n
__ a __ e	__ ow __

Read the words in the box. Then read the sentences. Find the word in the box that correctly completes each sentence. Write the word on the line.

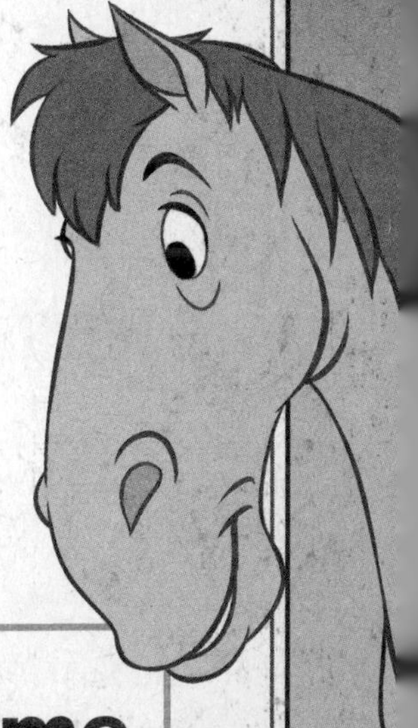

She came ____________ .

She ____________ in.

came
down

Say the word at the top of each box. Then fill in the missing letters.

were	they
_ _ _	_ _ _
_ e _ e	th _ _ y
_ _ _	_ _ _
w _ r _	_ h _ y

Read the words in the box. Then read the sentences. Find the word in the box that correctly completes each sentence. Write the word on the line.

They all came _____ .

They _____ work.

They _____ not there.

_____ came to work.

always
were
They
together

Cinderella

be

always

came

could

did

do

down

go

got

had

he

in

it

know

not

of

one

open

said

she

the

they

to

together

© Disney

was

© Disney

were

© Disney

who

© Disney

will

© Disney

work

© Disney

you

would

ANSWER KEY

Page 26

Page 27

Page 28

Page 29

Page 30

Page 31

Page 32

Page 33

Page 34

ANSWER KEY

ACTIVITY 1

Say the word at the top of each box. Then fill in the missing letters.

will — wi**ll**
will

make — make
make

you — **y**ou
you

work — work
wo**r**k

said — s**ai**d
s**ai**d

Page 64

ACTIVITY 2

Say the word at the top of each box. Then fill in the missing letters.

it — i**t**
it

ran — **r**an
ran

Read the words in the box. Then read the sentences. Find the word in the box that correctly completes each sentence. Write the word on the line.

Belle **ran** home.

It ran.

He will go **home**.

It
home
ran

Page 65

ACTIVITY 3

Say the word at the top of each box. Then fill in the missing letters.

very — very
very

big — b**ig**
b**ig**

Read the words in the box. Then read the sentences. Find the word in the box that correctly completes each sentence. Write the word on the line.

It **was** big.

He was not **very** big.

You said it was **big**.

Was **it** big?

very
was
big
it

Page 66

ACTIVITY 4

Read the words in the box. Then read the sentences. Find the word in the box that correctly completes each sentence. Write the word on the line.

Belle **let** him go.

The Beast will **go** home.

Let **him** go!

him
let
go

Page 67

ACTIVITY 5

Trace the name with your pencil. Then write the name on your own.

Belle   Belle

Say the word at the top of each box. Then fill in the missing letters.

would — would
wou**l**d

be — be
be

his — h**i**s
h**i**s

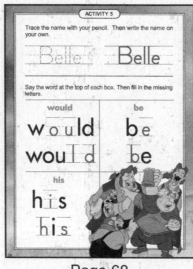

Page 68

ACTIVITY 6

Read the words in the box. Then read the sentences. Find the word in the box that correctly completes each sentence. Write the word on the line.

He will stop **them**

Stop them!

He **had** to stop.

He had **to** go home.

had
to
Stop
them

Page 69

ACTIVITY 7

Say the word at the top of each box. Then fill in the missing letters.

hurt — hu**r**t
hurt

was — was
w**a**s

Read the words in the box. Then read the sentences. Find the word in the box that correctly completes each sentence. Write the word on the line.

He will not be hurt.

He **was** hurt.

Belle will be **hurt**

He
hurt
was

Page 70

ACTIVITY 8

Read the words in the box. Then read the sentences. Find the word in the box that correctly completes each sentence. Write the word on the line.

It was **not** his.

There he was.

The Beast **was** not at home.

The Beast was big.

not
There
The
was

Page 71

ACTIVITY 9

Say the word at the top of each box. Then fill in the missing letters.

so — so
so

am — am
am

said — said
said

Belle — Belle
Belle

Page 72

ANSWER KEY

ACTIVITY 1

Say the word at the top of each box. Then fill in the missing letters.

run	away
run	away
run	away

Read the words in the box. Then read the sentences. Find the word in the box that correctly completes each sentence. Write the word on the line.

She could **run** fast.

She wanted to run.

She did not run **away**.

She **wanted** to run.

wanted
She
away
run

Page 102

ACTIVITY 2

Say the word at the top of each box. Then fill in the missing letters.

could	not
could	not
could	not
stop	them
stop	them
stop	them

Page 103

ACTIVITY 3

Say the word at the top of each box. Then fill in the missing letters.

they	could
they	could
they	could

Read the words in the box. Then read the sentences. Find the word in the box that correctly completes each sentence. Write the word on the line.

They did not run.

They did **not** show it to him.

They **could** not work.

They
not
could

Page 104

ACTIVITY 4

Trace the name with your pencil. Then write the name on your own.

Aladdin

Aladdin

Read the words in the box. Then read the sentences. Find the word in the box that correctly completes each sentence. Write the word on the line.

Aladdin **said** to run.

It **is** Aladdin.

Aladdin said to stop **it**.

is
it
said

Page 105

ACTIVITY 5

Read the words in the box. Then read the sentences. Find the word in the box that correctly completes each sentence. Write the word on the line.

He could not stop **me**.

He let me run away.

He did not **let** me stop.

He wanted to **show** me.

show
He
me
let

Page 106

ACTIVITY 6

Trace the name with your pencil. Then write the name on your own.

Jafar   Jafar

Say the word at the top of each box. Then fill in the missing letters.

he	took
he	took
it	it
it	it

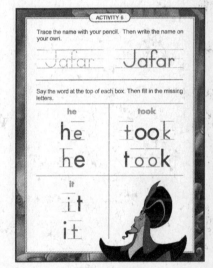

Page 107

ACTIVITY 7

Read the words in the box. Then read the sentences. Find the word in the box that correctly completes each sentence. Write the word on the line.

That did not work.

Jafar's plan did not **work**.

That is **not** work.

He **did** not run.

work
did
That
not

Page 108

ACTIVITY 8

Say the word at the top of each box. Then fill in the missing letters.

think	fast
think	fast
think	fast

Read the words in the box. Then read the sentences. Find the word in the box that correctly completes each sentence. Write the word on the line.

Aladdin had to **think**.

He wanted to run **fast**.

He had **to** show them.

Aladdin **had** to stop.

had
think
fast
to

Page 109

ACTIVITY 9

Trace the name with your pencil. Then write the name on your own.

Jasmine   Jasmine

Say the word at the top of each box. Then fill in the missing letters.

then	
then	
then	
pick	I
pick	I
pick	I

Page 110

ANSWER KEY

Page 140

Page 141

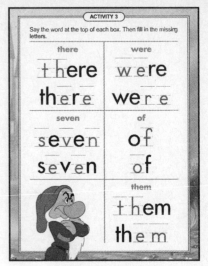

Page 142

Page 143

Page 144

Page 145

Page 146

Page 147

Page 148

ANSWER KEY

ACTIVITY 1
Say the word at the top of each box. Then fill in the missing letters.

want	to
want	to
want	to
be	**them**
be	them
be	them
said	
said	
said	

Page 178

ACTIVITY 2
Trace the name with your pencil. Then write the name on your own.

Prince Eric

Prince Eric

Read the words in the box. Then read the sentences. Find the word in the box that correctly completes each sentence. Write the word on the line.

I want to **sing**.

"I like Prince Eric," said Ariel.

I like them, **thought** Ariel.

Ariel will sing **for** Prince Eric.

| thought |
| I |
| sing |
| for |

Page 179

ACTIVITY 3
Say the word at the top of each box. Then fill in the missing letters.

she	to
she	to
she	to
see	**had**
see	had
see	had
him	
him	
him	

Page 180

ACTIVITY 4
Read the words in the box. Then read the sentences. Find the word in the box that correctly completes each sentence. Write the word on the line.

thought	Ariel	I
know	will	He

I want to sing.

I **know** Ariel.

He will sing for Ariel.

Ariel **will** sing for him.

I like to sing, Ariel **thought**.

"I know Prince Eric," **Ariel** said.

Page 181

ACTIVITY 5
Say the word at the top of each box. Then fill in the missing letters.

will	help
will	help
will	help
I	**he**
I	he
I	he
said	
said	
said	

Page 182

ACTIVITY 6
Say the word at the top of each box. Then fill in the missing letters.

over	boat
over	boat
over	boat

Read the words in the box. Then read the sentences. Find the word in the box that correctly completes each sentence. Write the word on the line.

She went **over** there.

He was in the **boat**.

Where was **the** boat?

He **went** over there.

| boat |
| the |
| over |
| went |

Page 183

ACTIVITY 7
Trace the name with your pencil. Then write the name on your own.

Ariel   Ariel

Say the word at the top of each box. Then fill in the missing letters.

help	they
help	they
help	they
had	
had	
had	

Page 184

ACTIVITY 8
Read the words in the box. Then read the sentences. Find the word in the box that correctly completes each sentence. Write the word on the line.

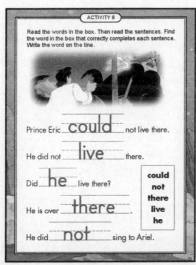

Prince Eric **could** not live there.

He did not **live** there.

Did **he** live there?

He is over **there**.

He did **not** sing to Ariel.

| could |
| not |
| there |
| live |
| he |

Page 185

ACTIVITY 9
Say the word at the top of each box. Then fill in the missing letters.

were	happy
were	happy
were	happy
	they
	they
	they

Page 186

237

ANSWER KEY

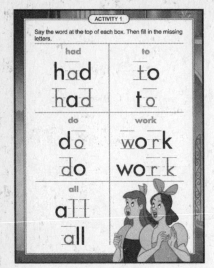

ACTIVITY 1

Say the word at the top of each box. Then fill in the missing letters.

had — had
to — to
do — do
work — work
all — all

Page 216

ACTIVITY 2

Read the words in the box. Then read the sentences. Find the word in the box that correctly completes each sentence. Write the word on the line.

She had to **open** it.

She had to do **it**.

She **did** not do it.

Did **she** open it?

She did **not** open it.

she
it
did
open
not

Page 217

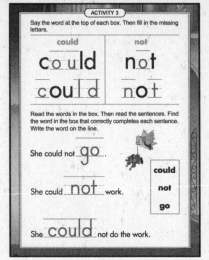

ACTIVITY 3

Say the word at the top of each box. Then fill in the missing letters.

could — could
not — not

Read the words in the box. Then read the sentences. Find the word in the box that correctly completes each sentence. Write the word on the line.

She could not **go**.

She could **not** work.

She **could** not do the work.

could
not
go

Page 218

ACTIVITY 4

Say the word at the top of each box. Then fill in the missing letters.

would — would
she — she

Read the words in the box. Then read the sentences. Find the word in the box that correctly completes each sentence. Write the word on the line.

She **said** she would do it.

She **would** open it.

She would do all the work.

would
She
said

Page 219

ACTIVITY 5

Say the word at the top of each box. Then fill in the missing letters.

she — she
not — not
did — did
know — know
he — he

Page 220

ACTIVITY 6

Say the word at the top of each box. Then fill in the missing letters.

in — it
got — got

Read the words in the box. Then read the sentences. Find the word in the box that correctly completes each sentence. Write the word on the line.

She **got** it.

Cinderella got **in**.

She could not go in.

got
in
She

Page 221

ACTIVITY 7

Say the word at the top of each box. Then fill in the missing letters.

it — it
be — be
will — will
one — one
you — you
of — of

Page 222

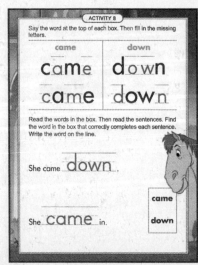

ACTIVITY 8

Say the word at the top of each box. Then fill in the missing letters.

came — came
down — down

Read the words in the box. Then read the sentences. Find the word in the box that correctly completes each sentence. Write the word on the line.

She came **down**.

She **came** in.

came
down

Page 223

ACTIVITY 9

Say the word at the top of each box. Then fill in the missing letters.

were — were
they — they

Read the words in the box. Then read the sentences. Find the word in the box that correctly completes each sentence. Write the word on the line.

They all came **together**.

They **always** work.

They **were** not there.

They came to work.

always
were
They
together

Page 224